LEARNING TOGETHER

CHALLENGE TESTS

Verbal Reasoning TEST 1

ADVICE AND INSTRUCTIONS ON COMPLETING THIS TEST

(PLEASE NOTE THAT THIS TEST MUST BE COMPLETED IN THE STANDARD WAY AND IS NOT IN MULTIPLE CHOICE FORMAT.)

1. **There are 100 questions in this test.**
2. **Start at question 1 and work your way to question 100.**
3. **If you are unable to complete a question leave it and go to the next one.**
4. **Do not think about the question you have just left as this wastes time.**
5. **If you change an answer make sure the change is clear.**
6. **Make sure you spell correctly.**
7. **You may do any rough work on the test paper or on another piece of paper.**
8. **This test should take approximately 50 minutes.**
9. **When you have finished this test mark it with an adult.**
10. **An adult may be able to explain any questions you do not understand.**

Published by Learning Together, 18 Shandon Park, Belfast, BT5 6NW. Phone/fax 028 90402086

e-mail: info@learningtogether.co.uk. Website:- www.learningtogether.co.uk

In a secret code 123456 means ORANGE.

1. What does 235 mean? (____________________)

In a secret code JLZTXF means FATHER.

2. What does TLZX mean? (____________________)

In a secret code 792168 means SAFETY.

3. What does 2961 mean? (____________________)

In a secret code FXZXJMOPX means VEGETABLE.

4. Write BEAT in code. (____________________)
5. Write BAGGAGE in code. (____________________)
6. Write GAVE in code. (____________________)
7. Write BATTLE in code. (____________________)

Paul is younger than Jane. Jane is older than Paul and Peter. Peter is not the youngest. List the children starting with the youngest.

8. (____________________) youngest
9. (____________________)
10. (____________________) oldest

Fred is not as tall as Sam or George. Sam is not the tallest. List the children starting with the tallest.

11. (____________________) tallest
12. (____________________)
13. (____________________) smallest

Six children Alan, Ann, Steven, Paul, Bob and Mary sit equally spaced around a circular table. Mary sits opposite Steven and on Ann's left. Neither Bob nor Alan sits between Steven and Ann. Alan is not beside Mary. Ann then changes places with Bob.

14 Who now sits opposite Ann? (________________)

15 Who now sits on Paul's left? (________________)

16 Who now sits furthest from Steven? (________________)

17 Who now sits on Mary's left? (________________)

18 Who now sits on Mary's right? (________________)

Six people from six different countries are on a train with six carriages. No two people are in the same carriage. The German has only two people behind him and the Russian has only two people in front of him. Neither the Irish nor Dutch passengers are in the first or last carriages. The Italian is in the first carriage. The Irish passenger is closer to the Italian than the French passenger.

List the people starting with the passenger in the last carriage.

19 (________________) Last carriage.

20 (________________)

21 (________________)

22 (________________)

23 (________________)

24 (________________) First carriage.

There are six houses in a street. They are built in two rows of three. Number one is opposite number two, number three is opposite number four and number five is opposite number six. Jones lives in the lowest odd numbered house opposite Stewart. Smith lives on the same side as Jones opposite Black. Black lives beside Grey but not beside Stewart. Brown lives in the other house.

25. Jones lives in house number? (____________)
26. Smith lives in house number? (____________)
27. Grey lives in house number? (____________)
28. Who lives in house number 2? (____________)
29. Who lives in house number 3? (____________)
30. Who lives in house number 6? (____________)

A man is standing in the North East corner of a square field, which has sides of 75 metres. He begins walking along the sides. He walks South, West and North and then stops.

31. In what direction would he have to walk to return directly to where he started? (____________)
32. How far is he from where he started? (____________)
33. What is the area of the field? (____________)
34. How much short of 400 metres has he walked? (____________)
35. If he walks 600 metres every 10 minutes, how long would it take him to walk right around the field? (____________)

A man tiles a wall with 50 square tiles. Each tile has sides of 20 centimetres. The wall is ten tiles high and 5 tiles long.

36. What length is the wall? (____________________)

37. What height is the wall? (____________________)

38. What is the area of the wall? (____________________)

39. If he uses square tiles of 10 centimetre sides, how many tiles would he need? (____________________)

Five children, Mary, John, Pat, Fred and Paul are racing toy cars. At the end of the race Pat finishes behind John but ahead of Paul. Paul finishes behind Mary but is not last. Mary finishes behind Pat but is also not last.

List how the children finish starting with first place.

40. (____________________) First place.

41. (____________________)

42. (____________________)

43. (____________________)

44. (____________________) Last place

In a cloakroom there are six pegs with coats on them. Pegs 1, 3 and 5 have ladies' coats and the rest have men's coats. Pegs 1 and 3 have grey coats, 2 and 5 have brown and the others black. Pegs 3, 5 and 6 are for short people and the others are for tall people.

45. Which peg is the short man's black coat on? (____________________)

46. 47. Which pegs have ladies' grey coats on them? (__________) & (__________)

48. Which peg is the short lady's grey coat on? (____________________)

Underline one word in each bracket.

49. The coat on peg 2 is owned by a (SHORT , TALL) (LADY , MAN).

50. The coat on peg 5 is owned by a (SHORT , TALL) (LADY , MAN).

Look at this diagram. (Not drawn to scale.)

It shows a circle inside a square.
The circle has a diameter of 4.5cms.
and a circumference of approximately 14cms.

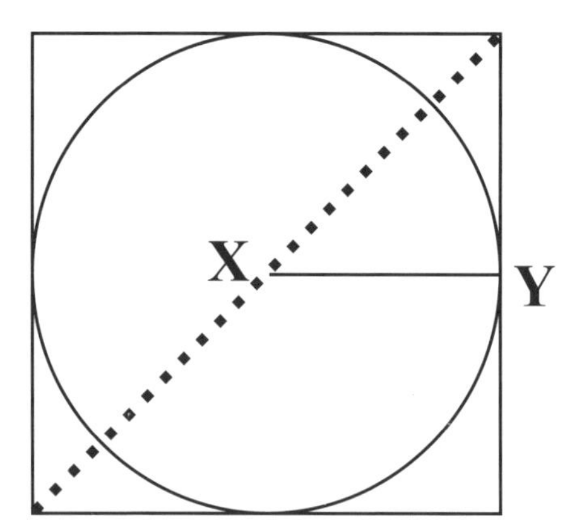

51 Which shape, the circle or square, has the greater area? (____________________)

52 What is the perimeter of the square? (____________________)

53 X is in the centre of the circle. What is the distance X to Y? (____________________)

54 What is the area of the square? (____________________)

55 What is the area of the right-angled triangle to the left of and above the dotted line? (____________________)

---

5 school classes V, W, X, Y and Z all have different numbers of pupils.
No school class has more than 35 pupils or less than 25 pupils.
Y has 5/6th of the number of pupils that W has and 5/7th of the number of pupils that Z has.
X has 3 pupils more than Y and 6 less than V.

56 How many pupils has class V? (____________________)

57 How many pupils has class W? (____________________)

58 How many pupils has class X? (____________________)

59 How many pupils has class Y? (____________________)

60 How many pupils has class Z? (____________________)

Six soldiers A, B, C, D, E and F are on parade and standing side by side in this order with A on the extreme left. B changes places with D and then with C. F changes places with A and then with C. D changes places with B and then with C and finally with F. A changes places with the soldier in A's original position. All the soldiers are now back in their starting positions.

61 How many times did A move? (________________)

62 How many times did B move? (________________)

63 How many times did C move? (________________)

64 How many times did D move? (________________)

65 How many times did E move? (________________)

66 How many times did F move? (________________)

Five trains depart from Hightown and arrive in Lowtown. All trains, except C, take the same time to complete the journey. There is a 7 minute gap between the arrival of one train and the departure of the next.
Using the information, given above, complete the table below.

		Depart Hightown	Arrive Lowtown
67	Train A		13.01
68	Train B	13.08	
69 70	Train C		
71	Train D	14.27	
72	Train E	15.09	

Five people A, B, C, D and E live in houses which are built with red brick or brown brick, and have either slates or thatch on the roof. Some people, but not all, own a dog. B and E are the only two who own dogs. A is the only person to use two colours of brick in his house. A and D have slates on their roofs, the others do not. E is the only other person who uses red brick.

73. Who lives in a red bricked house with a dog? (________________)

74. Who uses only brown bricks and slates for his house? (________________)

75. Which person has a dog, thatched roof and uses brown bricks? (________________)

76. Who uses thatch and brown bricks but does not own a dog? (________________)

X

Y

Look at this diagram. (Not drawn to scale.)

It is made up of squares of the same size.
The circle has a radius of 2.5cms.

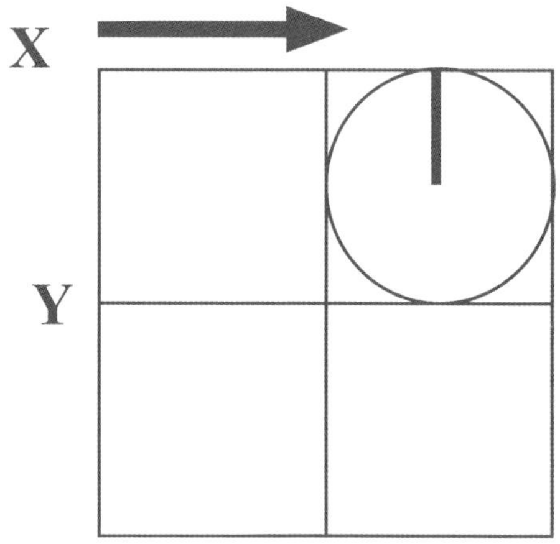

77. What is the length of one side of one square? (________________)

78. What is the total area of all four squares? (________________)

79. What is the perimeter of one small square? (________________)

80. A fly started at X and walked around the perimeter of the large square in the direction of the arrow.
How far would it have to walk before reaching Y? (________________)

81. How many square tiles of sides 1.25cms would be needed to cover the area of all four small squares? (________________)

The table below gives some information about four cars.
They all use the same price of fuel and all cars have the same fuel consumption.

Complete the table correctly.

	CAR	NO. OF LITRES TANK HOLDS	TOTAL COST TO FILL TANK	DISTANCE ON ONE TANKFUL
	A	20	£12.00	400KMS
82 83	B			370KMS
84 85	C		£13.20	
86	D	25	£15.00	

A number of people sit equally spaced around a circular table.
They are numbered in a clockwise direction and number 5 sits on the right of the person opposite number 15.

87 How many people are sitting at the table? (____________________)

88 Which number is sitting opposite number 4? (____________________)

89 Which number is sitting to the left of the person opposite number 7? (____________________)

90 If number 3 changed places with number 12 who would number 3 now be sitting opposite? (____________________)

Four children A, B, C and D are playing a board game in which they move counters along a board numbered 1-64.
The rules are as follows.
Throw a 6 to start and then put your counter on square number 5.
If a 2 is thrown, 6 is scored.
If a 6 is thrown, after the player has thrown his starting 6, zero is scored.
If a 5 is thrown, 3 is scored.
All other number are as shown on the dice.

Here are the first 6 throws of each child.

A	3	6	6	2	4	3
B	2	6	5	3	1	5
C	6	1	2	2	6	?
D	6	5	5	2	?	2

91 If C finished on 24 what was his last throw? (__________)

92 If D finished on 23 what was his 5th throw? (__________)

93 Who is furthest along the board? (__________)

94 What must B's next two throws be for him to reach 17? (_____&_____)

95 If A's next 3 throws are 5, 2 and 6, on what square does he finish? (__________)

Five children Paul, Lily, Sam, Beatrice and Mary are playing a game in which they give or receive sweets from each other. Paul gives Lily and Mary two sweets each and receives three from Beatrice and one from Sam. Sam receives one sweet from each player except Paul who gives him two. Beatrice gives Mary three sweets and receives four from Lily.

96 Paul finished with 15 sweets. How many did he start with? (__________)

97 Mary started with 12 sweets. How many did she finish with? (__________)

98 Sam finished with 8 sweets. How many did he start with? (__________)

99 Beatrice finished with 4 sweets. How many did she start with? (__________)

100 Lily started with 5 sweets. How many did she finish with? (__________)

LEARNING TOGETHER

CHALLENGE TESTS

Verbal Reasoning TEST 2

ADVICE AND INSTRUCTIONS ON COMPLETING THIS TEST

(PLEASE NOTE THAT THIS TEST MUST BE COMPLETED IN THE STANDARD WAY AND IS NOT IN MULTIPLE CHOICE FORMAT.)

1. **There are 100 questions in this test.**
2. **Start at question 1 and work your way to question 100.**
3. **If you are unable to complete a question leave it and go to the next one.**
4. **Do not think about the question you have just left as this wastes time.**
5. **If you change an answer make sure the change is clear.**
6. **Make sure you spell correctly.**
7. **You may do any rough work on the test paper or on another piece of paper.**
8. **This test should take approximately 60 minutes.**
9. **When you have finished this test mark it with an adult.**
10. **An adult may be able to explain any questions you do not understand.**

Published by Learning Together, 18 Shandon Park, Belfast, BT5 6NW. Phone/fax 028 90402086
e-mail: info@learningtogether.co.uk. Website:- www.learningtogether.co.uk

Six shoppers E, F, G, H, I and J queue at a supermarket check-out.
E is four places in front of I.
H is three behind E.
F is nearer the front of the queue than J.
There are two shoppers in front of G and none behind I.
List the shoppers in the queue from first to last.

1. (_______) 1st
2. (_______) 2nd
3. (_______) 3rd
4. (_______) 4th
5. (_______) 5th
6. (_______) 6th

Five towns are situated close together. Town A is North East of town B and South East of town C. C is North of B and West of town D which is North East of A. Town E is South of D and East of B. Which direction is it from?

7. **Town C to town E.** (______________________)
8. **Town D to town B.** (______________________)
9. **Town A to town E.** (______________________)
10. **Town E to town C.** (______________________)

Five girls A, B, C, D and E played with counters.
At the beginning A, B and C had 12 counters each and D and E had 15 each.
A got 1 from C and 2 from E. B gave 4 to C and the same to A.
D got 1 from everyone else and E got 4 from D and gave 2 to B.

(11) Who ended with the same number she started with? (__________________)

(12) Who had the least at the end? (__________________)

(13)(14) Which two girls had the same number at the end? (_________&_________)

(15)(16) Which two girls had half the total number of counters between them at the end? (_________&_________)

There are six shops in a block – a shoe shop, a bakery, a grocer, a chemist, a hardware shop and a pet shop.
The bakery is three shops from the pet shop and one from the shoe shop.
The hardware shop is at one end of the block and four shops from the chemist.
The shoe shop is closer to the chemist than to the hardware shop.

List the shops starting with the hardware shop.

	(17)	(18)	(19)	(20)	(21)
Hardware shop					

A bus and a train make the same journey between two towns A and E. They stop at three towns on the way. The train leaves 1 hour and 20 minutes after the bus and arrives 25 minutes later than the bus.
It takes the bus the same length of time to travel from B to C as the train to travel from D to E. The train arrives at C 35 minutes after it leaves A and an hour after the bus. The bus takes 40 minutes more than the train to go from A to D.

Answer questions 22-27 by completing the table and then answer questions 28-33 that follow the table.

		BUS	TRAIN
22	TOWN A		10.10
	TOWN B	09.20	10.30
23 24	TOWN C		
25 26	TOWN D		
27	TOWN E	11.15	

28. At what time is the bus at C? (__________)

29. At what time is the train at D? (__________)

30. How much longer is the journey by bus from A to E? (__________mins_)

31. When the train leaves A which town is the bus travelling to? (__________)

32. Passengers travelled from A to E by bus. The bus broke down at C and they travelled the rest of the way by train.
How long did their total journey, including the wait, take? (__________)

33. At what time would the train need to leave A each day in order to arrive at E at the same time as the bus? (__________)

Alan, Betty, Chris, Dave and Edward are the five children in a family.
The youngest is older than 3 and the oldest is younger than 16. There are no twins in the family.
Two children are older than 11. All the ages, except Dave's, are an even number of years.
Alan is older than Chris and their ages together make Betty's age.
Edward is the youngest and Betty is the oldest.

Give each child's age below.

34 Alan is (______________________)

35 Betty is (______________________)

36 Chris is (______________________)

37 Dave is (______________________)

38 Edward is (______________________)

At the start of a race 6 greyhounds A, B, C, D, E and F are placed in a row of starting boxes.
The boxes are numbered 1 to 6.

1	2	3	4	5	6

Dog A is in the odd-numbered box next to dogs B and D.
Dog F is in an even-numbered box next to dog C.
Dog D is not in an odd-numbered box but is next to dog E.
Dog C is in a box at one end of the row.

What is the number of the box that contains:

39 Dog A? (_______)

40 Dog B? (_______)

41 Dog C? (_______)

42 Dog D? (_______)

43 Dog E? (_______)

44 Dog F? (_______)

A street has 8 houses numbered 1 to 8. The odd-numbered houses are opposite the even-numbered ones. Number 1 is opposite number 2 and so on.
Eight families A, B, C, D, E, F, G and H live in the houses.

F lives at one end of the odd row. E's number is twice that of H's.
D lives in an even-numbered house and G lives at one end of that row.
B and H live opposite one another. A lives next door to F.
The number of D's house is one more than the sum of H and B's houses.
The number of F's house is 3 more than that of B's house.

Give the number of each family's house.

45. Family A (__________)
46. Family C (__________)
47. Family E (__________)
48. Family G (__________)
49. Family B (__________)
50. Family D (__________)
51. Family F (__________)
52. Family H (__________)

F, G, H, I and J are 5 points on a map. I is 6km due south of F and 5km due east of G.
H is due east of F. J is 7km due east of I and directly south of H.

53. Which point is south-east of F? (__________)
54. Which point is north-east of I? (__________)
55. Which point is 12km due west of J? (__________)
56. If a man travels 7km east of F and then 6km south, at which point would he be? (__________)
57. If a man travels from G to H by going through I and F, how far is the journey? (__________km___)
58. If a man travels directly from J to G and then through I to F, how far is the journey? (__________km___)

Traffic signals have two sets of lights, one for drivers and one for pedestrians.

Set A: **Red, green and amber for drivers.**

Set B: **Green man and red man lights for pedestrians.**
Pedestrians cross when the green man shows.

The following settings occur one after the other and then the pattern is repeated.

	RED	AMBER	GREEN	GREEN MAN	RED MAN
Drivers stop.	ON	OFF	OFF	ON	OFF
Drivers prepare to stop.	ON	ON	OFF	OFF	ON
Drivers go.	OFF	OFF	ON	OFF	ON
Drivers stop.	OFF	ON	OFF	OFF	ON

59 A driver approaches red and amber lights.
When these lights change which man will light up for pedestrians? (________________)

60 When the red man is not on, which light for drivers must be on? (________________)

61 When the same colour is showing for both drivers and pedestrians, what other colour is showing? (________________)

62 When three of the five lights are on is it safe for pedestrians to cross? (________________)

63 If the green man is showing, which colour for drivers would be on? (________________)

In each of the following questions one word can be put in front of each of the four given words to form a new word. Write the correct word in the brackets.

Look at this example: board berry out bird (BLACK)

64. town pour cast stairs (____________)
65. sick work land less (____________)
66. burn day rise set (____________)
67. coat over table stile (____________)
68. ward roar set stairs (____________)
69. word able age port (____________)

At a party six chairs are placed in 2 rows opposite one another.
In one row the chairs are numbered 1, 3 and 5.
In the opposite row they are numbered 2, 4 and 6.
Chair 1 is opposite chair 2.
Chair 3 is opposite 4 and chair 5 is opposite 6.
Six children A, B, C, D, E and F sit on the chairs.
F is on an even-numbered chair opposite to E but he does not sit on chair number 6.
A is not beside B, and D is not beside E.
A and D sit on centre chairs.

Music is played and the children change seats.
C changes with F.
E changes with D.
B and A change.

70. Who sits on chair number 4? (____________)
71. On which chair does F sit? (____________)
72. On which chair does D sit? (____________)
73. Who sits opposite C? (____________)
74. Who sits on chair number 3? (____________)

Dot, Amy and Helen each have a blouse, skirt and a scarf. Each garment is black, yellow or white. No two garments of the same type have the same colour. Each girl wears garments of 3 different colours.
Dot's scarf is the same colour as Helen's skirt.
Amy's scarf and Dot's skirt are both the same colour as Helen's blouse.
Amy's skirt is yellow and her blouse is not black.

75. What colour is Amy's blouse? (____________________)

76. What colour is Dot's skirt? (____________________)

77. What colour is Helen's scarf? (____________________)

78. Which girl has the black blouse? (____________________)

79. Which girl has the white scarf? (____________________)

Together 5 children have £8.00.
The girls together have exactly the same amount as the boys together.
Sue has 50p more than Olive. Len has 60p more than Fred.
Dave has the same as Len and Fred together.

How much do they each have?

80. Sue has (£____________)

81. Olive has (£____________)

82. Dave has (£____________)

83. Len has (£____________)

84. Fred has (£____________)

A, B, C, D, E and F are six boats sailing due East in a race.
E is due East of A. B is due East of E and due West of F.
C is due North of B. D is due South of E.

85. Which boat is leading the race? (________________)

86. Which boat is last in the race? (________________)

87. How many boats are further to the East than E? (________________)

88. Which boat is sailing furthest North? (________________)

89. Which boat is sailing furthest South? (________________)

A digital watch gained time at a steady rate. A man set it to the correct time when he got up in the morning. When the lunchtime news started at 13.00 the watch showed 13.10. Four hours later it showed 17.18.

90. What time did the watch show when the correct time was 11.00? (________________)

91. When it was 6 o'clock in the evening what time did the watch show? (________________)

92. When the watch showed 16.16 what was the proper time? (________________)

93. At what time did the man get up in the morning? (________________)

94. How many minutes does the watch gain each hour? (____________mins__)

Three men and three women are sat equally spaced around a circular table. No two men were sitting together. Lisa was opposite Tom. Joan sat opposite Peter with Tom on her right. Also at the table were Sandra and Harry. After a while some of them changed seats. Joan and Harry changed seats with each other and so did Tom and Sandra.

95. Which woman was then beside Peter? (________________)

96. Who was then on Harry's left? (________________)

97. Who was then opposite Sandra? (________________)

98. 99. Name the two men who were then sitting together. (____________&____________)

100. Who was then opposite Joan? (________________)

LEARNING TOGETHER

CHALLENGE TESTS

Verbal Reasoning TEST 3

ADVICE AND INSTRUCTIONS ON COMPLETING THIS TEST

(PLEASE NOTE THAT THIS TEST MUST BE COMPLETED IN THE STANDARD WAY AND IS NOT IN MULTIPLE CHOICE FORMAT.)

1. **There are 100 questions in this test.**
2. **Start at question 1 and work your way to question 100.**
3. **If you are unable to complete a question leave it and go to the next one.**
4. **Do not think about the question you have just left as this wastes time.**
5. **If you change an answer make sure the change is clear.**
6. **Make sure you spell correctly.**
7. **You may do any rough work on the test paper or on another piece of paper.**
8. **This test should take approximately 50 minutes.**
9. **When you have finished this test mark it with an adult.**
10. **An adult may be able to explain any questions you do not understand.**

Published by Learning Together, 18 Shandon Park, Belfast, BT5 6NW. Phone/fax 028 90402086

e-mail: info@learningtogether.co.uk. Website:- www.learningtogether.co.uk

A man sells consecutively numbered tickets from a roll of tickets.
The first number he sells is 0234 and the last ticket he sells is 0436

1. How many tickets did he sell ? (__________)

2. If he had sold 300 tickets what would have been the number of the next ticket NOT sold? (__________)

Six boys A, B, C, D, E and F sit equally spaced around a circular table. D sits on A's right and opposite E. C sits between A and E. B sits on the left of the person opposite A.
B then changes places with A and C changes places with D.

3. Who now sits on the left of B ? (__________)

4. Who now sits opposite the person on the left of D ? (__________)

5. Who is furthest away from B ? (__________)

F leaves the room and the rest of the boys change seats. A and E change places, B moves to the seat opposite.
E moves 2 seats to the left and C moves to an empty chair.

6. Who is sitting to the left of an empty chair? (__________)

7. Who is sitting between B and D ? (__________)

8. F returns and sits at the table. Who is on his left? (__________)

In each line below, the first word can be changed into the last word in three stages.
Only one letter can be replaced at a time and proper words must be made each time.
An example has been done to help you.

tide (ride) (rode) rope

9. **hail** (__________) (__________) **pull**

10. **pink** (__________) (__________) **cane**

11. **fact** (__________) (__________) **lake**

12. **kerb** (__________) (__________) **head**

13. **chin** (__________) (__________) **shop**

The numbers on a die (a single dice) are covered by 6 different letters of the alphabet.

Four of the letters are vowels.
The letter I is the only vowel that covers an even number.
The number 2 is covered by the letter that comes immediately after the third vowel used.
The sum of the numbers, which are covered by consonants, is 6.
The first and last letters of the alphabet are used and the sum of the numbers they cover is 7.
The largest odd number is covered by the vowel that is nearest to the middle of the alphabet and the other vowels appear near the beginning of the alphabet.

Beside each number below write the letter that covers it on the die.

14 1. Letter (______)

15 2. Letter (______)

16 3. Letter (______)

17 4. Letter (______)

18 5. Letter (______)

19 6. Letter (______)

5 kings Alfred, Charles, William, Harold and George all had different amounts of money.

William is not the richest or the poorest but is richer than at least 2 other kings. Alfred is only richer than one other king and that is not Harold or George. George is poorer than 1 other king and that is not Charles.

List the kings from richest to poorest.

20 (______________________) Richest

21 (______________________)

22 (______________________)

23 (______________________)

24 (______________________) Poorest

A number of people sit evenly spaced around a circular table. They are numbered consecutively in an anti-clockwise direction. Number 9 sits opposite the person who is two places to the left of number 6.

25 How many people are at the table? (__________)

26 Which number is opposite number 1 ? (__________)

27 Which number is beside number 2 and opposite number 8? (__________)

28 29 Number 3 and number 9 change places.
Which two numbers now sit beside number 10 ? (________&________)

The numbers 1, 2, 3, 4, 5, 6 and 7 are used in code form to produce the words:

BRASH ERASER RASHER SHARP PHRASE

One of the words uses 1, 2, 3, 4 and 5 for its first five letters. Two of the words have a 3 for their last but one letter. A five-letter word begins with 6.

30 What is PHRASE in code? (____________________)

31 What is ERASER in code? (____________________)

32 What is BRASH in code? (____________________)

33 What word does 152751 represent? (____________________)

34 If an 8 means L then what word does 75218 represent? (____________________)

35 What word does 82658 represent? (____________________)

4 boys Peter, Andrew, Mark and Billy build model cars from parts that are red, blue, green and yellow. The cars have tyres, radios, boots and bonnets. Each car contains 4 parts and each part is a different colour. There is only one part of each colour and no car contains any two parts that are the same colour.

Andrew's tyres are the same colour as Peter's radio and Mark's bonnet.
Andrew's boot is yellow.
Mark's radio is the same colour as Peter's boot and Andrew's bonnet.
Peter's tyres and Billy's bonnet are red.
Mark's radio is green.

36 **Who has a car with a blue radio?** (______________)

37 **Who has a car with green tyres ?** (______________)

38 **Who has a car with a yellow bonnet?** (______________)

39 **What colour are Mark's tyres ?** (______________)

40 **What colour is Peter's bonnet?** (______________)

41 **What colour is Billy's radio?** (______________)

A man is tiling a tabletop using rectangular and square plastic tiles. He uses a pattern like that shown in the diagram. The rectangular tile" A" measures 15 x 5 cms.

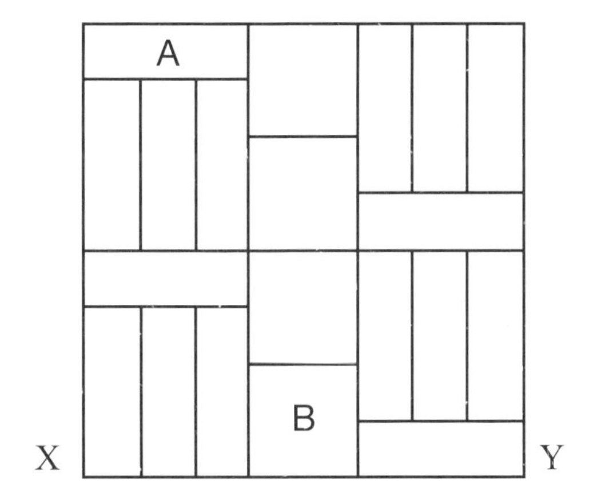

42 What is the distance X ⟶ Y? (_______cm)

43 What is the area of a square tile B ? (________ sq.cm)

44 How many tiles would be needed if the sides of the pattern were trebled in length? (__________tiles)

45 The man finds that he can only buy square tiles which measure 5 x 5 cms. He cannot buy rectangular tiles. How many small square tiles would he need to fill the diagram above? (__________tiles)

5 people A, B, C, D and E choose 5 coloured balls from a black bag and after counting their score they put the balls back in the bag and allow the next person to choose.
The bag contains 4 red, 3 blue, and 2 green and 6 white balls.
If a person chooses a green (G) ball he scores 5.
If a person chooses a red (R) ball he doubles the score of his next ball. Consecutive red balls count as one ball.
If a person chooses a white (W) ball he scores 1.
If a person chooses a blue (B) ball he trebles the score of the ball he chose immediately before he chose the blue ball.
The person with the highest score wins the game.

The people chose these balls:

A.	**G**	**B**	**W**	**W**	**R**
B.	**R**	**G**	**W**	**W**	**B**
C.	**R**	**R**	**G**	**W**	**B**
D.	**W**	**W**	**R**	**G**	**?**
E.	**R**	**R**	**W**	**G**	**G**

46 What was C's score? (__________)

47 Who won the game? (__________)

48 If D scored 12, what colour was his last ball ? (__________)

49 50 Which two people had the same score? (_____&_____)

5 cars Saab, Nissan, Ford, Porsche and Renault take part in a car race. The Saab finishes 3 minutes ahead of the Nissan but is not first. The Porsche finishes 4 minutes behind the Ford but only 1 minute behind the Saab. The Renault is as far behind the Porsche as the Ford is in front of the Porsche.

51 Which car is third? (__________)

52 Which car is last? (__________)

53 How many minutes separate the second and the fifth cars? (__________)

54 How many minutes separate the Nissan and the Ford cars? (__________)

55 Which car is first? (__________)

8 people sit equally spaced around and facing a circular table. There are four boys numbered 1, 2, 3 and 4. There are four girls lettered A, B, C and D. No two boys and no two girls sit side by side.
3 is beside B on her left and opposite 4.
C is not beside number 4 or number 1.
D sits two seats away from B.

56. Who sits opposite B ? (________________)

57. Who sits beside 1 on his left? (________________)

58. Who sits on the right of the person opposite D? (________________)

59. Is a boy or girl opposite the person two places to the left of the person opposite A? (________________)

60. Who sits between C and A and opposite 1? (________________)

61. Who sits beside 4 on his left? (________________)

Four boys Alan, Bill, Colin and David each receive four gifts of a toy car, a bicycle, a book and a ball. There are four of each toy and each toy comes in one of four colours. The colours are yellow, red, green and blue. Each boy has four different coloured toys and no two boys have the same toy in the same colour.
Alan's car, Bill's ball and Colin's bicycle are all the same colour. David's book is yellow. Colin's car, Bill's bicycle and Alan's book are all the same colour. David's ball is green and his bicycle is not red. Bill's car is blue and his book is not yellow or green. Colin's book is blue.

62. **Who has a blue ball and a red bicycle?** (________________)

63. **Who has the green bicycle?** (________________)

64. **What colour is Colin's ball?** (________________)

65. **What colour is Bill's bicycle?** (________________)

66. **Who has a red book?** (________________)

67. **Who has a green car?** (________________)

Five garages A, B, C, D and E have a different number of cars for sale. No garage has less than 3 cars or more than 12 cars. The total number of cars is 36. Only one garage has an even number of cars for sale.

The cars of D and E added together give 2 more than C's cars. D has 3 times as many cars as B who has 4 less than A.

68 How many cars has A for sale? (________________)

69 How many cars has B for sale? (________________)

70 How many cars has C for sale? (________________)

71 How many cars has D for sale? (________________)

72 How many cars has E for sale? (________________)

Six children stand equally spaced in a circle and are numbered from 1 to 6 in a clockwise direction. Number 2 stands between 1 and 3.
Number 3 stands between 2 and 4, and so on.
The smallest odd number and the largest even number change places.
The other two odd numbers then change places. The two numbers which add together to make a total of 4 change places.
Finally the two numbers that add to make 10 change places.

73 Which number did not change to a different position? (________________)

74 Which number finished where number 5 started? (________________)

75 Which number finished where number 1 started? (________________)

76 Which number finished standing between 6 and 2? (________________)

77 Which number finished standing between 1 and 4? (________________)

Five children, A, B, C, D and E have each saved a different amount of money. No one has saved less than £20 or more than £30.
A has £3 more than C but less money than D.
Only A and E have an even amount of money.
B has the smallest amount, which is £7 less than E has.
Only one child has saved more than E.
How much has each child saved?

78 A has saved (£________________)

79 B has saved (£________________)

80 C has saved (£________________)

81 D has saved (£________________)

82 E has saved (£________________)

Four girls, Ann, Betty, Clare and Dawn played a game using the face of a clock. Each girl had a counter which was moved around the numbers on the clock face.

RULES

A die (a single dice) was thrown and the number shown was the number on which the counter was placed. No further move was made at this first throw.
Two more throws were made by each girl. If an odd number was thrown, the counter was moved anti-clockwise that number of moves. If an even number was thrown, the counter was moved clockwise the number shown on the die.

The game began and each girl threw a different number with her first throw. No one threw a 4 or a 1 at this stage. All Ann's throws were even numbers and she finished on number 10 on the clock face. Her second and third throws were the same.
Clare finished on number 2. Her first and third throws were odd numbers and her second throw was a 4. Dawn threw three different odd numbers. Betty threw the same number each time and finished where she started.

83 On which number did Dawn finish? (________________)

84 On which number did Betty finish? (________________)

85 What was Ann's second throw? (________________)

86 What was Clare's third throw? (________________)

f each girl had been given one more throw

87 What would Dawn have needed to finish on number 5 ? (________________)

88 What would Betty have needed to finish on number 1 ? (________________)

Six children, A, B, C, D, E and F stand equally spaced in a circle. They face into the centre of the circle.
Another child G, stands in the centre of the circle.
G is looking directly at B.
D is between A and F.
A is not standing next to B nor is directly behind G.
E is standing to the left of A.

89 Who is standing directly behind G? (________________)

90 Who is to the left of F? (________________)

91 Who is to the right of F? (________________)

92 93 Apart from B, which two children can G see? (________________)

In a car park there are 250 cars.
The cars are coloured BLUE, WHITE, RED, YELLOW and BLACK. For every blue car there are four white cars.
There are twice as many red cars as white cars.
For every yellow car there are three white cars.
There are as many black cars as there are yellow and blue cars together.

How many cars are there of each colour?

94 BLUE CARS (________________)

95 WHITE CARS (________________)

96 RED CARS (________________)

97 YELLOW CARS (________________)

98 BLACK CARS (________________)

Four children W, X, Y and Z each have a different number of felt tipped pens.
No one has more than 15 or less than 8.
W has the most and 2/3 more than Y.
Z has 2 more than Y.
X has a 1/3 of the total of W and Y added together.

99 How many felt tipped pens has Z? (________________________)

100 How many felt tipped pens has Y? (________________________)

LEARNING TOGETHER

CHALLENGE TESTS

Answers

Preparation for Verbal Reasoning in Eleven plus tests, Twelve plus tests and grammar school selection examinations.

This book contains 3 tests each containing 100 questions and answers and gives practice in extended Verbal Reasoning questions of the type found in many eleven plus and twelve plus examinations.

These extended questions are a type of Verbal Reasoning question that many children (and adults) find difficult.

This question type requires the child to deal with a number of pieces of information at the same time and this can be very demanding. (A grid may assist the child to put the information into a simpler format.)

Verbal Reasoning involves the child thinking about words and text and solving problems, sequences etc all mostly related to language. It requires the pupil to have a good grasp of English grammar and a wide vocabulary. In some Verbal Reasoning selection tests there may be some number based questions such as number sequences or inserting a missing number.

Most schools and Local Authorities administer at least one Verbal Reasoning test.

You should check requirements with your Local Authority or school

ANSWERS TO LEARNING TOGETHER CHALLENGE TEST
PAPER NUMBER 1

1	RAG	**51**	SQUARE
2	HATE	**52**	18 cm
3	FATE	**53**	2.25 cm
4	OXMJ	**54**	20.25 sq cm
5	OMZZMZX	**55**	10.125 sq cm
6	ZMFX	**56**	34
7	OMJJPX	**57**	30
8	PAUL	**58**	28
9	PETER	**59**	25
10	JANE	**60**	35
11	GEORGE	**61**	2
12	SAM	**62**	3
13	FRED	**63**	3
14	PAUL	**64**	4
15	BOB	**65**	0
16	MARY	**66**	4
17	ANN	**67**	12.26
18	BOB	**68**	13.43
19	FRENCH	**69**	13.50
20	DUTCH	**70**	14.20
21	GERMAN	**71**	15.02
22	RUSSIAN	**72**	15.44
23	IRISH	**73**	E
24	ITALIAN	**74**	D
25	1	**75**	B
26	5	**76**	C
27	4	**77**	5 cm
28	STEWART	**78**	100 sq cm
29	BROWN	**79**	20 cm
30	BLACK	**80**	35 cm
31	EAST	**81**	64
32	75M	**82**	18.5 L
33	5625 sq m	**83**	£11.10
34	175m	**84**	22 L
35	5 mins	**85**	440 kms
36	1 metre (100cms)	**86**	500 kms
37	2 metres (200cms)	**87**	18
38	2 sq m (20,000sq cms)	**88**	13
39	200	**89**	17
40	JOHN	**90**	12
41	PAT	**91**	2
42	MARY	**92**	6
43	PAUL	**93**	C
44	FRED	**94**	1 and 1
45	6	**95**	27
46,47	1 and 3 (any order)	**96**	17
		97	16
48	3	**98**	4
49	TALL MAN	**99**	7
50	SHORT LADY	**100**	2

ANSWERS TO LEARNING TOGETHER CHALLENGE TEST PAPER NUMBER 2

1	F	51	7
2	E	52	3
3	G	53	J
4	J	54	H
5	H	55	G
6	I	56	J
7	SOUTH EAST (SE)	57	18 km
8	SOUTH WEST (SW)	58	23 km
9	SOUTH EAST (SE)	59	RED
10	NORTH WEST (NW)	60	RED
11	D	61	AMBER
12	B	62	NO
13,14	C & E (any order)	63	RED
15,16	A & D (any order)	64	DOWN
		65	HOME
		66	SUN
17	GROCER	67	TURN
18	BAKERY	68	UP
19	SHOE SHOP	69	PASS
20	CHEMIST	70	E
21	PET SHOP	71	5
22	08.50	72	1
23	09.45	73	D
24	10.45	74	B
25	10.35	75	WHITE
26	11.15	76	BLACK
27	11.40	77	YELLOW
28	09.45	78	HELEN
29	11.15	79	DOT
30	55 minutes	80	£2.25
31	D	81	£1.75
32	2 hours 50 minutes	82	£2.00
33	09.45	83	£1.30
34	8	84	£0.70 or 70p
35	14	85	F
36	6	86	A
37	13	87	3
38	4	88	C
39	5	89	D
40	6	90	11.06
41	1	91	18.20
42	4	92	16.00
43	3	93	08.00
44	2	94	2 mins
45	5	95	LISA
46	1	96	JOAN
47	6	97	LISA
48	2	98,99	PETER & TOM (any order)
49	4		
50	8	100	TOM

ANSWERS TO LEARNING TOGETHER CHALLENGE TEST PAPER NUMBER 3

1	203	**51**	Porsche
2	534	**52**	Renault
3	D	**53**	5mins
4	C	**54**	6 mins
5	F	**55**	FORD
6	E	**56**	A
7	A	**57**	B
8	E	**58**	3
9	Hall Hull *	**59**	GIRL
10	Pine Pane*	**60**	2
11	Face Lace*	**61**	D
12	Herb Herd*	**62**	ALAN
13	Chip Ship*	**63**	BILL
14	E	**64**	RED
15	J	**65**	GREEN
16	A	**66**	BILL
17	Z	**67**	COLIN
18	O	**68**	7
19	I	**69**	3
20	HAROLD	**70**	12
21	GEORGE	**71**	9
22	WILLIAM	**72**	5
23	ALFRED	**73**	2
24	CHARLES	**74**	1
25	10	**75**	4
26	6	**76**	5
27	3	**77**	3
28,29	3 & 1 (any order)	**78**	26
		79	21
30	741235	**80**	23
31	512351	**81**	29
32	61234	**82**	28
33	REAPER	**83**	1
34	PEARL	**84**	6
35	LABEL	**85**	4
36	PETER	**86**	5
37	BILLY	**87**	4
38	PETER	**88**	5
39	YELLOW	**89**	D
40	YELLOW	**90**	D
41	YELLOW	**91**	C
42	40cms	**92,93**	E & C (any order)
43	100sq. cms		
44	180 tiles	**94**	15
45	64 tiles	**95**	60
46	13	**96**	120
47	A	**97**	20
48	RED	**98**	35
49,50	D & E (any order)	**99**	11
* other answers may be possible		**100**	9

Published by Learning Together, 18 Shandon Park, Belfast, BT5 6NW. Phone/fax 028 90402086
e-mail: info@learningtogether.co.uk. Website:- www.learningtogether.co.uk